MINDFUL MANTRAS:

I Matter

By Laurie Wright

Illustrations by Dave Jacquith

Dedicated to all the kids in all the world -
you all matter more than you will ever know!

(There are 16 of these little guys in this book, can you find them all?)

My name is Elise, and I matter.

In the morning, I wake up and I play with my baby brother. When he laughs, and smiles and looks happy, I know that I matter.

I MATTER.

After breakfast I carry my dishes to the sink and I put away the milk. I help my Dad tidy the kitchen, and when he says thank you and smiles at me, I know that I matter.

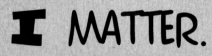

Before I leave for school, I notice that the plants need water, so I get the watering can and give them a drink.

When the blooms instantly look bigger and brighter, I know that I matter.

I MATTER.

My brother is feeling sick, so I give him a stuffy and a blankie to make him feel better.

When he lets out a happy sigh, says thank you and looks comforted, I know that I matter.

If my friend feels sad, I smile at her, give her a hug and tell her a funny story.

When her tears stop, and she looks relieved and smiles, I know that I matter.

I MATTER.

Sometimes my teacher needs help to keep the classroom clean, so I push in the chairs and sweep up the floor.

When she tells me I am a great helper, gives me a big smile and a look of appreciation I know that I matter.

I MATTER.

At the park I see a little baby crying and upset. I walk over and make a funny face at him and he laughs!

WAHH!!!

When he stops crying and gives a sweet baby giggle, I know that I matter.

I MATTER.

After school my mom is so excited to see me! I give her a BIG hug and a kiss, and I tell her about my day.

When she asks me questions about my day, smiles SO big, and listens to me talk, I know that I matter.

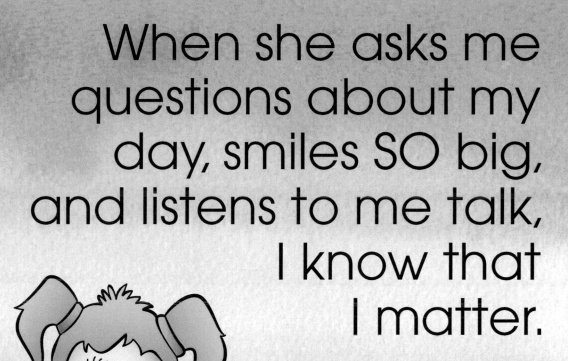

I MATTER.

I notice after dinner that my dog's water bowl is empty, so I fill it up!

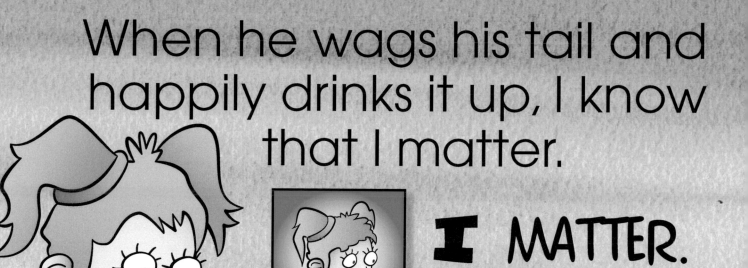

When he wags his tail and happily drinks it up, I know that I matter.

I MATTER.

As I lay in bed and think about my day, I realize that in so many ways, **I matter.**

My name is
Elise

AND **I** MATTER!

My name is

_____

AND **I** MATTER!

Laurie Wright is a Canadian speaker, author, and educator who is passionate about helping children increase their positive self talk and improve their mental health. After writing and publishing "I Can Handle It", a book that helps kids handle their everyday problems, Laurie realized there was more work to be done!

"I Matter" is the second book in an ongoing series designed to help children increase their positive self talk, self esteem, and confidence. Laurie is determined to help children learn to believe in themselves and to realize how very important they all are.

Dave Jacquith is a freelance illustrator with over 35 years experience in the graphic arts industry. He is a graduate of the school of everyday life resulting in the enjoyment of seeing and living in the world that surrounds him. Being able to express that love of life with art is what makes Dave want to get up in the morning (well, mid-morning) and see what the day will bring. Working on this book with Laurie has been an experience of immense pleasure and satisfaction.

Made in the USA
San Bernardino, CA
21 April 2017